Worzel Gummidge in
PIGEON POST

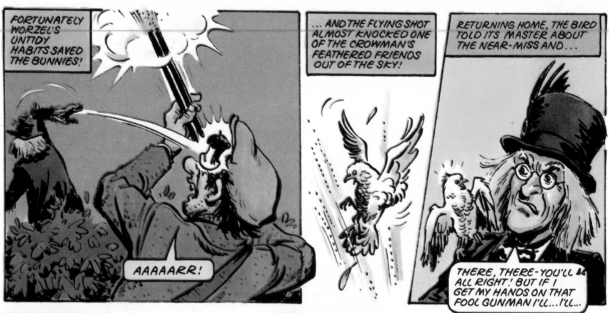

FORTUNATELY WORZEL'S UNTIDY HABITS SAVED THE BUNNIES!

AAAAARR!

... AND THE FLYING SHOT ALMOST KNOCKED ONE OF THE CROWMAN'S FEATHERED FRIENDS OUT OF THE SKY!

RETURNING HOME, THE BIRD TOLD ITS MASTER ABOUT THE NEAR-MISS AND...

THERE, THERE - YOU'LL BE ALL RIGHT! BUT IF I GET MY HANDS ON THAT FOOL GUNMAN I'LL...I'LL...

MEANWHILE...

MERCY! HAVE MERCY... I'M ONLY AN OLD SCARECROW!

SUDDENLY, WORZEL REALISED HE WAS NOT THE TARGET!

'E'S 'OPPIN' IT FAST! WONDER IF 'E'S SCARED OF BEIN' CAUGHT! THIS NEEDS LOOKIN' INTO A-FORE I'M BLOWN TO STRAW!

THAT SAME AFTERNOON, JOHN AND SUE STOPPED TO EXAMINE SPRING FLOWERS MAKING A WELCOME APPEARANCE ON THE ROAD VERGE...

THEY'RE SO FRESH AND BRIGHT!

MAKES ME THINK ABOUT EASTER AND A SCHOOL HOLIDAY! HEY, HERE COMES MR. CROWMAN...

GOOD DAY, CHILDREN. HAVE YOU SEEN ANYBODY CARRYING A GUN RECENTLY?

WELL MR. BRAITHEWAITE WAS CLEANING HIS SHOTGUN YESTERDAY!

NOT RIGHT ORF, MR. CROWMAN! I WAS RUNNIN' YOU SEE! BUT I'D MAKE A GOOD GUESS!

THAT YOU WOULD, WORZEL! YOU'D PICK ANYBODY PASSING THROUGH TO GET INTO MY GOOD BOOKS!

THE CROWMAN'S PARTING REMARK MADE WORZEL JUMP FOR JOY!

I'M GOING TO FIND THAT PIGEON MENACE, WORZEL! AND I'D BE ETERNALLY GRATEFUL FOR ANY HELP I GOT FROM WHATEVER SOURCE!

THAT'S IT! I'LL FIND THE DANG-BLASTED VILLAIN AN' HIS MAJESTY THE CROW-MAN WILL TAKE GOOD CARE OF ME! HEY-HEY! WHAT A GRAND DAY!

ABOUT AN HOUR LATER ...

WORZEL SEEMS HAPPY!

THAT MEANS HE'S UP TO MISCHIEF, I'LL WARRANT!

A HUNTIN' WE WILL GO! A HUNTIN' I WILL GO! HE-HO-WHEREVER 'E GOES, I'LL CATCH 'IM!

COME ON, LET'S FIND OUT WHAT HE'S UP TO!

I HAVE NEVER SEEN HIM MOVE SO FAST- NOT SINCE AUNT SALLY THREW THOSE ROCKS AT HIM, THAT IS!

WORZEL KNEW WHERE TO COLLECT HIS IMFORMATION ...

'DAY TO YOU, TURNIP-HEAD! EXCITIN' AIN'T IT? CHASIN' A MAN WITH A GUN ...

YOU'RE CHASIN' 'IM, WORZEL? 'E'S BEEN GONE... ER... LET'S THINK... ER ... LONG, LONG TIME!

THAT BE 'IM, RIGHT ENOUGH! WHICH WAY?

ER ... THERE ... THAT WAY! OOER, ER ... WAS IT THAT WAY? YES, THAT WAY!

MEANWHILE...

WHAT A ROTTEN DAY IT'S BEEN - NARRY A BIRD OR BEAST! POACHIN' AIN'T WHAT IT USED TO BE, I'LL TELL THE WORLD!

Aunt Sally

1

2

3

Magnificent trees of all shapes and sizes grace our countryside, parks and fields. Can you match the names and illustrations .... answers page 59

TREES

7

8

9

4

5

6

TEASE

Common Oak, Field Elm, Scots Pine, Spruce, Sweet Chestnut, Holly, Hornbeam, Silver Birch, Larch, Mountain Ash, Cedar, Lombardy Poplar.

10

11

12

THE step by step creation of that famous scarecrow face begins early each morning on the set, as Jon Pertwee settles in front of the mirror with make-up artist Marion Durnford, and the ninety minute ordeal with glue, paint, mud, and more begins . . .

The changin
face o

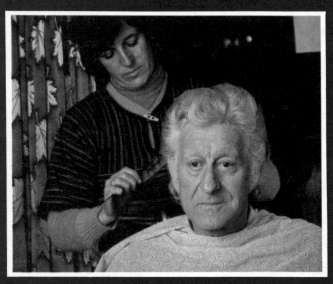

Marion refers to continuity photographs which were taken on the first day of shooting, so that she gets the make-up the same every day . . .

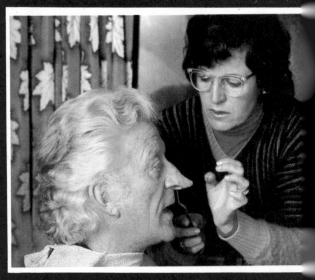

First to go on is the nose, which is made of latex rubber. A new nose is used every day. It is fixed into position with liquid rubber which takes half an hour to set . . .

While the nose dries, the basic face colour is applied. Worzel's "normal" head is that of a mangold worzel, which is reddish-orange. Jon's eyes are heavily outlined, too.

Next come the whiskers on his chin, and for those Marion uses rea carrot roots. The eyebrows are fashioned from genuine ears of corn fixed into place with spirit gum . . .

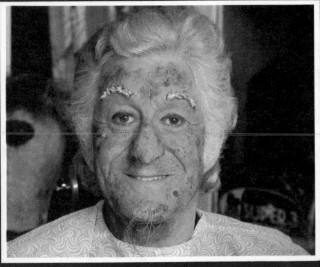

All the mud on the face is a blend of real mud and brown watercolour paint. Marion builds it up in layers, and as it fades during the day she

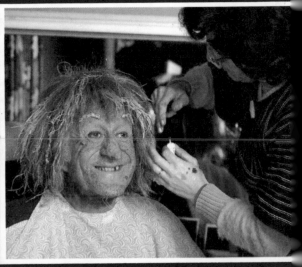

Finally, on goes the wig, which is flecked with straw. The transform ation is complete, and Jon Pertwee, as Worzel Gummidge, is ready t

Jon Pertwee

ALMOST HUMAN

THE THREAT

WORZEL GUMMIDGE did not feel good. He was suffering from exposure. A rather vicious old rook had caught him unawares and plucked a large beakful of hay from his chest. He felt so bad, in fact, that he just hung around Ten Acre Field on his pole for most of the morning.

When Farmer Braithewaite came along and saw Worzel's condition he tut-tutted and haphazardly stuffed a tattered handkerchief in the scarecrow's 'wound' and walked off to attend to his cattle.

"Tis bad enough bein' 'is scarecrow but the way 'e insults me is fit to make Worzel Gummidge up an' find a new job!" the scarecrow said to the circling rooks.

Looking down at his chest, Worzel felt even more incensed. The handkerchief stuck out a corner like a tongue permanently giving the world a raspberry. It was too much, and easing himself from his pole he stalked away.

Near the hedgerow which bordered the field there was a compost heap. Worzel's face went *pale* and he hurriedly skirted the heap. He knew what The Crowman did with scarecrows who had outlived their usefulness – dug them into a compost heap!

Towards the other end of Ten Acre Field, Worzel met Upsidaisy. Even he had to admit that Upsidaisy looked peculiar with those three legs that had once belonged to a milking stool doing weird things to the scarecrow's walk.

"Don't try to comfort me, Upsidaisy'" said Worzel.

"I wasn't doin' the like," Upsidaisy replied.

"Good!" Worzel said and stomped away.

"Hey, wait for me," cried Upsidaisy.

"No time," Worzel called, putting distance between them. "Silly ol' moo-stool," he muttered under his breath, bad tempered as a scarecrow could get.

At that very second, John and Sue came

into sight carrying a hamper. The minute they saw Worzel, John said: "Oh-ho, here comes a problem."

Sue smiled. "Worzel's no problem if we give him something to eat."

Worzel heard the magic word *EAT* and stopped in his tracks. He would need all the energy he could find to make the long, long journey to the next county. He was determined to start a new life for himself and had the cunning to realise that anywhere within tricycling range of The Crowman meant near doom. A compost heap end to all his ambitions.

"Look at him," John chortled, keeping the hamper safely out of Worzel's reach. "He's fit to nosh the lot."

Worzel tried to appear regal. It was a difficult task with that handkerchief corner sticking from his chest but he thought he did a rather excellent job of drawing himself up to his full height.

"Don't be a tease, John," Sue scolded, opening the hamper.

Worzel's eyes lit up. What a lot of goodies. Sandwiches, milk, apples, cake . . . He could hardly wait to tuck in.

"Are you hungry?" Sue asked, fingers closing on a sandwich.

"Oo, ar . . . is Worzel hungry? Ye ask me that?"

"I didn't," John remarked acidly.

Worzel's eyes fastened on the boy and indignantly dismissed the other. An expression of low cunning crossed his face next and he forced a smile for Sue.

"You can't have it all," the girl said, handing over a sandwich. "We're going on a picnic."

Worzel flopped to the ground and ate his sandwich. He would miss the children. Glancing about him, he realised that he would miss everything and everybody in Scatterbrook. If only the farmer could regard him as an important 'person'. A very important 'person'.

John pointed at Worzel's chest and asked, "What have you been doing to yourself? That looks ridiculous."

Worzel silently accepted a small cup of milk, cleared his throat and got to his feet. He did a funny bow for Sue's benefit and turned his back on John. All the deviousness he possessed went into his walk then. He deliberately staggered as if weak and near exhaustion. He weaved and tottered and waited for the children to run to his aid.

"Oh, boy, can he ever put it on," John's voice said behind him.

"Shush, he'll hear you," Sue whispered.

Worzel turned, all haughty. "I did 'ear 'im," he snapped. "You just wait till I collapses an' Mr. Crowman is called . . ."

"I wouldn't call him," John chuckled. "I'd simply dig you into a compost heap."

Compost heap again! Worzel wondered if the world had suddenly taken leave of its senses. It was as if he had turnip-blight and been declared a dustbin cast-off.

"He's teasing you, Worzel," Sue said, trying not to laugh.

"I am, Worzel," John said, face serious. He didn't like the way the scarecrow was reacting. It was so untypical Worzel Gummidge.

One thing could always change a disgruntled Worzel into a happy Gummidge and the scarecrow came forward, without so much as a 'by your leave', and began plucking food from the hamper.

Sue eyed John and silently warned him not to upset Worzel again. Together, they watched as Worzel tucked in – all notions of having a picnic feast gone now.

When he had emptied the hamper, Worzel patted his stomach. "Tain't your fault," he said mysteriously to the children and relaxed.

"What isn't?" John asked, puzzled.

"I'll tell ee," Worzel said, leaning against a tree trunk. He touched the handkerchief in his chest and presented a woeful face for sympathy. "I'm leavin' ee . . . goin' far, far away."

Sue began to smile. "Don't be silly, Worzel – you couldn't. Why, who would stuff you when . . ."

Worzel frowned. "Stuff? Stuff?" He flipped the protruding corner of the handkerchief. "Ye call this stuffin'?" he asked.

John gazed down at the remains of their picnic meal – a few crumbs and discarded wrappers. "I call what you just did stuffing!"

"John!" Sue admonished.

"Okay, okay, I'm sorry, Worzel – but you really do eat too much. And anyway, Sue's right – you can't leave Scatterbrook. The Crowman would be very, very annoyed." John wagged a finger under Worzel's nose. "And that could mean . . ."

"You'll get me all muddled," Worzel complained. "I wish I had me thinkin' head on . . ."

John bent over the scarecrow and patiently explained. "I meant that Mr. Crowman would follow you, find you and then . . ." He sighed and acted the role of a man digging.

"The compost heap!" Worzel cried in alarm.

"You two," Sue moaned and cleared up the mess Worzel had made. She closed the hamper and took a few steps in the direction of the Braithewaite farm. "Be good, Worzel . . . go back to your own field."

John laughed and took off after his sister. "She's right, Worzel," he called. "You better be good and get back to work 'cause if you don't . . . Well . . ." and he made that digging gesture again.

Poor Worzel! The scarecrow was genuinely worried, and confused. So much time had elapsed since his decision to leave the county that he doubted now if he could make the next community before nightfall. It was bad enough being alone in your own field during the darkness but to be wandering strange fields and narrow lanes where even the foxes, badgers and owls were unknown left him in a blue funk.

"If there was some way . . ." Worzel started to think, scratching his head in dismay.

A noise nearby made Gummidge look up. He almost quaked with fright. There was no mistaking that top hat, nor the face beneath it.

"Oo! Oo! Oo! Your 'igh an' mightiness . . ." he blubbered, leaping erect and showing signs of doing a bunk.

"*Worzel!*" The Crowman's voice sounded very strict.

Worzel froze, eyes rolling in terror.

"And where do you think you are going?" Mr. Crowman asked.

"I . . . I . . . I . . ." the scarecrow stammered.

The Crowman's eyes fixed on Worzel's chest and a little smile touched his lips. "Ah-ha, you've been letting those rooks get the jump on you again."

"Ar! Oo! Ee doesn't know the half of it, sir!" Worzel blurted.

The Crowman nodded thoughtfully and, without a moment's hesitation, seized Worzel and flung him over his shoulder. To

Worzel's disgrace he was carried to the Crowman's tricycle and dumped into it . . .

John and Sue watched as Mr. Crowman cycled past them, lifting his hat in recognition, and continued along the road with Worzel's arms and legs flopping from the tricycle's back trailer.

"I hope it isn't the end for old Worzel," John said slowly.

"You . . . you horrid boy," Sue yelped. "Don't dare even think like that." She was worried though and her eyes were moist as she watched the tricycle fade into the distance . . .

The sun had vanished behind the horizon and the moon hung high in silvery splendour above Scatterbrook and the surrounding countryside. The night was so still, and a mixture of scents came from the flower-beds near the Braithewaite farm. For John and Sue the beauty of the night had lost its meaning. They sat on a stone wall, silent and tense.

Finally, Sue asked, "Do you think Worzel's been really dug into a compost heap, John?"

"I don't know," John replied, feeling a lump in his throat. He wished that he hadn't threatened Worzel that afternoon.

"We could ask Mr. Crowman . . ." Sue fidgetted.

"That wouldn't do any good," John said. "If the worst has happened all the asking in the world won't replace Worzel."

"Replace Worzel?" a voice asked behind them. "Oo's replacin' Worzel?"

John felt a terrible weight lift from his young shoulders. Sue jumped down from the wall and swung around, eyes shimmering.

Worzel Gummidge stood there, bathed in moonlight. He did not look much different except for the brand new straw filling the cavity in his chest.

"Worzel, it's you!" Sue cried.

"'course it's me," the scarecrow snapped, full of his old arrogance.

"What . . . what?" John tried to ask.

Worzel waved away questions and shuffled past. "Don't put me in no compost heap yet, young 'uns," he said with a high and mighty tone of voice. "Worzel Gummidge is too important to be throwed away. Ask Mr. Crowman if ye don't believe ar . . ."

When the scarecrow was out of ear-shot, John grinned. "He's incredible!" he stated.

Sue nodded thoughtfully and gazed at the warm light coming from the farmhouse windows. "Come on," she said. "If we get a good night's sleep perhaps we can have that picnic to-morrow. The way Worzel's feeling he won't be cadging off us . . ."

"I wouldn't count on that!" John replied, following her.

As for Worzel – well, he was on his pole settling in for a night's sleep, too. Dreaming already of another picnic hamper and all those lovely goodies the children liked to 'provide' for his enjoyment.

OUT OF ORDER

The four pictures below are not in the proper sequence. Can you work out the correct running order?   Answer page 59

FROM THE COMFORT OF THEIR ROOM, JOHN AND SUE ANXIOUSLY WATCH THE STORM'S FURY...

POOR OLD GUMMIDGE! I WONDER IF HE'S SAFE?

WORZEL'S NOT SLOW AT PROTECTING HIMSELF!

BUT...

TAIN'T FITTIN' FOR A SCARECROW LIKES ME TO SUFFER SUCH INDIGNITIES!

SUDDENLY...

OOOOOO, ARRRR! HEEEEEELP!

AND AS THE TREE FELL, IT TRAPS A SCARED, STRUGGLING SCARECROW!

MERCY! OO, MR. CROWMAN, SIR — PLEASE COME AN' SAVE ME!

SOMEBODY DID CARE... JOHN AND SUE — AND NOT JUST FOR WORZEL GUMMIDGE, EITHER!

WE'VE GOT TO HELP THEM ALL, JOHN! I COULDN'T REST EASY THINKING HOW THEY'LL BE WASHED AWAY!

FIGHTING THE STORM, THE CHILDREN MANAGE TO FIND HANNAH HARROW...

OVER HERE, HANNAH — YOU'LL BE SAFE!

WITH HANNAH AND SEVERAL OTHER SCARECROWS SAFE, THE CHILDREN WORKED THEIR WAY TO TEN ACRE FIELD...

OH, JOHN — LOOK! IT'S POOR OLD WORZEL!

I...CAN'T HOLO....THIS....MUCH ...LONGER!

I'M A-DONE FOR! I'M WASHIN' AWAY...

ONE LAST EFFORT AND SUE DRAGGED WORZEL FREE!

THERE! YOU'RE OKAY, WORZEL!

PHEW — ABOUT TIME! I'M WHACKED!

YEEEOW, CAREFUL — 'EE'S BREAKIN' ME BACK-STIFFENER!

STOP COMPLAINING, WORZEL!

WE'VE GOT TO LEAVE YOU, WORZEL — BUT I'LL SLIDE THIS BAR ACROSS TO KEEP THE COWS OUT!

THAT'S RIGHT! LEAVE ME ALONE! DON'T WORRY 'BOUT ME INSIDES COMIN' OUT AN' FIELD MICE WAITIN' TO CRAWL INTO ME ELBOWS!

AFTER FIVE HOURS THE RAINS CEASED AND SCATTERBROOK COUNTED ITSELF LUCKY TO ESCAPE WITH MINOR FLOODING!

BY THE NEXT DAY, MRS. BLOOMSBURY-BARTON WAS ORGANIZING AN APPEAL...

WE MUST DO SOMETHING FOR ALL THE HOMELESS! I SUGGEST COLLECTIONS ON A GRAND SCALE...

SHE WOULD! I THINK SHE'S OUT FOR A MEDAL!

THIS IS WHAT I PROPOSE, LADIES! WE EACH PICK A CORNER AND CARRY A BOX LIKE THIS...

DISASTER FUND

WE COULD ALSO RUN A JUMBLE SALE — THAT'S A POPULAR FORM OF FUND RAISING!

FOR JOHN AND SUE, THOUGH, HELP WAS NOT JUST FOR PEOPLE!

AND THEY'RE ALL IN NEED OF ATTENTION, MR. CROWMAN!

ESPECIALLY WORZEL GUMMIDGE — HE'S UNABLE TO STAND!

AND SO, THE FOLLOWING DAY...

BE THANKFUL, YOU LOT — THOSE CHILDREN RISKED THEIR LIVES FOR YOU!

IS ME ROBIN REDBREAST RIGHT'S AS RAIN, SIR?

GENTLY TAKING THE ROBIN FROM WORZEL'S STOMACH THE CROWMAN TALKED TO IT...

TAIN'T FAIR MAKIN' MOCK O' ME A-FORE THAT LITTLE TWEETIE! NOR TAIN'T MY FAULT I WAS NEAR FLOATED ORF!

A SMART BIRD LIKE YOU OUGHT TO FIND A BETTER HOME BUT I SUPPOSE YOU'RE HAPPY!

TO YOUR POST, WORZEL HEDGEROW GUMMIDGE!

EE EXPECTS ME TO STAND IN THAT THERE MUD! I'D GET MILDEWED FEET, SURE AS EGGS ROT!

THE MINUTE MR. CROWMAN'S TRICYCLE VANISHED FROM SIGHT, WORZEL LEFT HIS POST!

HA, NOW FOR A DRY PLACE AN' SOMETHIN' TO EAT!

DOWN ON THE FARM
PICTURE CROSSWORD.

ALL THE CLUES ARE SHOWN OPPOSITE. Ⓐ = ACROSS Ⓓ = DOWN. Solutions p.59

THE ACCUSATION

VERY soon it would be harvest thanksgiving. Sue looked forward to this. She enjoyed decorating the village church and celebrating the end of harvest.

John did not find the event very exciting. As he told one of his friends, "It's only another time for singing songs." He much preferred to think of harvest's end as the long run-in towards Christmas. As a time when football boots came out and week-end soccer went back on the telly.

For the farmers of Scatterbrook it was a period of uncertainty. So many things could make or break a harvest; most of all the weather. Farmer Braithewaite, like his neighbours, inspected the skies every morning when he awoke. The slightest sign of dark clouds on the horizon was enough to cause a minor breakfast table upheaval. Like . . .

"Never mind my meal," the farmer shouted, grabbing his hat.

"Sit down, *dear*," his wife ordered. "You know how peckish you gets if you dash off without a decent breakfast."

"But . . ." the farmer tried to explain, eyes darting to the window and those growing clouds.

"You'll work better with bacon an' eggs inside you," the woman said and straight away heaped his plate.

Farmer Braithewaite knew better than to prolong any argument with his loving wife. Anyway, all the other country signs pointed to a settled day. He sat at the table and sighed. She did cook some fantastic meals . . .

Out in the middle of Ten Acre Field, Worzel Gummidge felt his anger grow. He loathed harvest. With all those noisy tractors and shouting farm labourers around it was almost the last straw for a scarecrow.

Several rooks lazily circled Worzel's scarecrow pole and made good use of the air currents.

"Stewpit bundles o' feathers!" Worzel roared. When the rooks continued to circle he took a deep breath and yelled at the top of his voice: "You all got cloth ears or somethin'? I said shooh! SHOOH!"

The rooks, if they heard, ignored him. Fact was, the rooks were so accustomed to Worzel Gummidge's tantrums and sulks that they seldom bothered to glance in his direction any more. Mind you, they did not land near him. He still scared them – at close range. But not when they were airborne or pecking seed near the the other side of the field.

"I've 'ad 'em," Worzel muttered and eased off his pole. "An' I'm in no mood to listen to tractors today . . ." And with that he strode away.

He had no idea where he was going, but then Worzel frequently took a few hours off-duty to pursue certain scarecrow pleasures. Places like Scatterbrook village's main street attracted Gummidge. Especially those shops catering for his tastes in food. Without going to the village a scarecrow could find decent snacks and milk to drink. So many people left bottles of milk on their doorsteps it was surprising that the entire scarecrow population wasn't waterlogged. Or so Worzel thought.

The lane made a sharp turn by an old Victorian letterbox and Worzel was about to follow the road when he heard a strange noise. He paused, and that probably saved him from a dustbin.

Siren wailing, horn blaring, a police car screamed round the bend and zig-zagged as its driver tried to straighten the vehicle out. Worzel gave a squeal, and dived into the hedgerow. He felt the rush of air as the car passed, smelt its exhaust fumes and then . . .

A person describing what happened next would have said about the 'black void' and losing consciousness and a lot of other wild imaginings. A scarecrow, however, did not get knocked unconscious. Nor were there black voids to fall into. *What really happened* was that Worzel's head got jammed in a rabbit hole.

Later on, when asked by his sergeant, the police car driver said of the 'accident', "S'truth, sarge – how was I to know it was a man? All I saw was this bundle of hay . . ."

Luckily, Worzel Gummidge was not present when this remark was made. Worzel Gummidge was an instrument of a devious plot to extract cash from the police funds. For once, an innocent victim of another man's greed.

The person who could make Worzel appear innocent had to be a near genius. Which was an apt way of saying that one Herbert Jackson McEnerie rated rave notices in the *Police Gazette* for being the best confidence trickster in Britain. Bar none.

Herb, as his crook mates called him, happened to be walking along the country lane when Worzel did his magnificent dive into the rabbit hole. He watched in amazement. He expected the police car to stop – but it didn't. He expected an enraged man to emerge from the hedge-ditch and chase after the car. But Worzel was stuck fast in a new world of utter darkness.

Herb went to Worzel's aid. His first shock was when he grabbed those kicking legs and found himself gripping bundles of straw. Unable to believe what he felt and saw, Herb relentlessly pulled until . . .

Plop!

"Yeeeoooooow!" Worzel yelled in agony. Clapping hands to his head he pressed down on it. Mr. Crowman may swop heads for me occasionally, he thought, but I don't want a new one under these circumstances!

Herb peered and paled.

"What's wrong?" Worzel asked.

"You . . . you . . . you're not . . ." Herb could not find the words.

"'Tis bad enough nears as losin' me head without ye losin' your tongue," Worzel stated. "Speak up."

Herb gulped and found courage. "You're not a man . . ."

"Scarecrow," Worzel admitted without rancour.

"A scarecrow?" Herb's voice rose to a shriek.

"Sounds like 'em would scare the rooks," Worzel said.

Before the startled crook could regain his speech, John and Sue rounded the bend and gazed at Worzel. "Hi," said John.

"Hello, Worzel," said Sue.

Herb blinked owlishly. "Did you both say hello to that?" he asked.

"Yes," the children said together.

"But it's . . ." the con man began.

"I'm," Worzel corrected.

"A scarecrow!" Herb finished in a whisper.

"Oh, you know!" John said.

"Worzel doesn't usually go around telling everybody what he is," Sue said.

"A scarecrow!" Herb repeated, much louder. More interested.

Worzel glared at the stranger. He was testy at the best of times but this was getting him down faster than an express train. Or a dive into a rabbit hole. "Excuse us," he said to Herb, and drew the children to one side. "Who's 'e?" he asked in a stage whisper.

"I don't know," John replied.

"He's a stranger," Sue said.

"I knows that," Worzel snapped. "Where's 'e from?"

"How can you tell where a stranger is from?" John asked.

Worzel's expression suggested a fit of the sulks not far away. "Stewpit!" he said.

Herb interrupted them. "You were almost killed," he told Gummidge.

John laughed and Sue said, "He can't be killed. He can be dug into a compost heap. Or chucked in a dustbin. Or turned into a haystack. But not killed, sir."

The subtle differences escaped Herb. "That police car wasn't to know what it missed . . ."

Worzel said, "Barmy!"

Herb's cunning came to the fore. "Did you see the accident?" he asked the children.

"We heard the car, saw it almost turn-over on the bend," John replied.

"Aye," Worzel growled. "'e crazied till he got 'er straight."

"They should pay for your injuries . . . er, is that right?" Herb could not get used to the situation.

"Mr. Crowman would know," Sue said to John.

"No, not 'is 'ighness," Worzel wailed. The mention of The Crowman sent him into spasms of jelly-like fear.

"All right, Worzel," Sue soothed. "Though why you get so uptight when he's mentioned makes me suspicious."

"I ain't done nothin' bad," Worzel swore.

"That's as maybe," John said. "But you have – in the past."

"He be makin' mock o' Gummidge," the scarecrow snapped, fear gone.

Herb begged, "Can't we talk about the terrible accident?"

"Who got hurt?" Sue asked in all innocence.

"Him . . . er, it!" Herb indicated Worzel.

"Were you?" John asked.

Worzel felt his head. It seemed secure if a little bashed where a small stone had dug in. "I'm right as grade 'A'," he replied. Then he recalled what the stranger had said earlier about a payment. "'course, if they wanted to pay . . ."

"Worzel, that's cheating," Sue accused.

"Worse," John said firmly. "It's downright illegal. The police would have you on a charge."

"They can't charge a scarecrow," Worzel said defiantly.

And that was when Herb departed. He went directly to the police and, pretending to be the accident victim's brother-in-law, suggested that a small *ex gratia* payment could halt a case for dangerous driving reaching the courts.

The sergeant was a canny Scot, a man not given to making a payment on anything until he either had the goods in his hands or the concrete evidence written on an official form. He told Herb he would investigate the affair and to call back later. His tone of voice just may have suggested to Herb that a payment would be forthcoming.

Once Herb went to find a cafe the sergeant drove to the so-called scene of the accident. He discovered a few bits of hay, straw, an old worn scarf and a small piece of turnip by the mouth of a rabbit hole . . .

The next day, Worzel was out foraging for goodies when he bumped into John and Sue again.

"Remember that funny stranger we met yesterday?" Sue asked.

"Yes," Worzel replied, not really interested.

"The police have him locked up in a cell," John exclaimed.

"Ooooo!" Worzel spotted a toffee paper sticking from John's breast-pocket.

"He was a crook," Sue explained. "He wanted the police to pay for your accident . . ."

"Pay?" Worzel suddenly heard and was interested. "Pay in what? Toffees? Cream cakes?"

"Money," John sighed. "And here – it's yours." He took the single toffee from his pocket and gave it to Worzel. "I haven't any more."

Worzel popped the sweet into his mouth.

"That stranger accused you of complicity," Sue mentioned.

"Compliccy what?" Worzel said round his chewy toffee.

"Forget it," John groaned and they went away leaving Worzel puzzled.

Country Jokels

WORZEL GUMMIDGE in
FOUR·FOOTED FEAR

MANY OF SCATTERBROOK'S SCARECROWS GOT WORZEL HEDGEROW GUMMIDGE'S MESSAGE AND SET OUT TO ATTEND THE MEETING HE HAD CALLED!

TWO KITCHEN GARDEN SCARECROWS WERE LESS THAN ENTHUSIASTIC, THOUGH ...

CAN'T THINK WHY WE BE GOIN' 'COS IT DON'T CONCERN US!

WORZEL WAS AWARE HE HAD SOME OPPOSITION!

THEY AIN'T GOIN' TO GET THEIR INSIDES EATEN' 'COS THEY AIN'T WHERE A-BODY'S AT THE MERCY O' CERTAIN CRITTERS!

WHY, I'VE HEARD TELL THEY'RE KNOWN TO EAT TIN CANS! TIN CANS! AN' WE AIN'T MADE O' TIN!

FRIENDS, WE MUST UNITE AGAINST THIS ENEMY! THERE'S NO TELLIN' 'OW MANY O' US THEY'LL EAT 'FORE THEIR STOMIKS ARE FILLED!

WHAT CAN WE DO? TELL US, GUMMIDGE!

DRIVE 'EM OUT! AR, THAT'S WHAT TO DO — DRIVE 'EM OUT!

EASIER SAID THAN DONE, WORZEL!

BUT...

SAVE ME, WORZEL! ONE DIDN'T GO—AND IT'S GOT A HUNGRY LOOK IN 'IS EVIL EYE!

OOOOO, EE SAVED ME, WORZEL!

WOTS THIS, THEN? SOMETHIN' HAS SCARED 'EM, SIR! BUT NO MATTER, THEY WON'T BE BOTHERIN' YOU AGAIN, EH?

I SINCERELY TRUST NOT, CONSTABLE! YOU COULD MAKE AN OFFICIAL REQUEST THAT THEY BE CONFINED TO A FENCED PADDOCK!

IF ONLY THE HUMANS KNEW HOW MUCH THEY OWED TO A SCARECROW...

SOMETHIN' SCARED THEM BUT I DON'T INTEND TO LOOK TOO HARD FOR THE CAUSE!

PHEW! I KNOWS THIS MUCH—IF ONE OF 'EM NANNY-GOATS COMES BACK I'LL MAKE AN 'AYRICK OUT OF IT! 'FORE IT MAKES A MEAL O' ME!

The Crowman

6. Fox
   Pine Marten
   Polecat

7. Short-tailed Vole
   Brown Rat
   Water Shrew

8. Hare
   Rabbit

9. Red Deer
   Fallow Deer
   Roe Deer

10. Quail
    Partridge
    Pheasant

1. Stoat
Weasel
Ferret

2. Wood Mouse
House Mouse
Harvest Mouse

IDENTITY PARADE QUIZ

Can you identify these creatures from the options
given in each case?

Answers page 59

3. Falmate Newt
Common Lizard
Smooth Newt

4. Adder
Grass Snake
Slow Worm

5. Common Frog
Marsh Frog
Common Toad

CHANGING COUNTRYSIDE

As pretty as a picture, that's a popular description of the English countryside. Well, at first glance the two colourful scenes above appear to be identical — but look again, and try to spot the ten art changes to the lower picture.

Answers page 59

The Wedding...

...that didn't
go as planned!

WORZEL'S PARTY

CHRISTMAS IN SCATTERBROOK IS WHITE, CRISP AND FESTIVE. BUT FOR ONE INHABITANT THE SNOW IS UNWELCOME...

IT'S FINE FOR 'EM TO 'AVE PRESENTS AN' PLAY GAMES AN' SIT DOWN TO HEAPIN' MEALS BUT NARRY A ONE THINKS 'BOUT WORZEL GUMMIDGE ALL ALONE IN THE COLD!

WELL, IF'N THEM STEWPIT BUNDLES O' FEATHERS CAN CADGE FOOD, THERE'S NO REASON WHY I CAN'T, EITHER!

MEANWHILE, JOHN AND SUE WERE ENJOYING THE SNOW...

LET'S MAKE HIM LIKE WORZEL!

WHO EVER HEARD OF A SNOWMAN THAT LOOKS LIKE A SCARECROW? DON'T BE SILLY, THIS IS A CHRISTMAS-MAN!

OKAY, HAVE IT YOUR WAY! THIS PIPE SHOULD MAKE YOUR CHRISTMAS-MAN HAPPY!

AND MY HAT'LL KEEP HIS HEAD WARM!

THE SNOWMAN WAS ABOUT FINISHED WHEN WORZEL APPEARED ON THE SCENE!

LET'S FIND A COAT FOR HIM, EH?

GIRLS CAN BE SO STUPID! A COAT WOULD MELT THE SNOW!

GET 'IM A COAT! WORZEL'S FROZEN AN' COULD DO WITH A THICK COAT!

AS ONE, THE CHILDREN REACHED A DECISION!

WAIT, WORZEL! YOU CAN HAVE YOUR GIFT NOW!

IT WORKED!

THE CHILDREN TOOK WORZEL INTO A BARN WHERE THEY HAD THEIR MANY GIFTS FOR THE SCARE-CROW FAMILY...

STAND OVER THERE, WORZEL - AND NO PEEPING!

I KNOW THIS MUCH- AN' IT'S A FACT- THEM THERE PRESENTS AIN'T ALL FOR EE, WORZEL GUMMIDGE! SOME OTHER BODY'S GETTING WHAT YOU'D LIKE!

HAPPY CHRISTMAS, WORZEL! I HOPE YOU'LL LIKE THIS!

AND THIS!

YE SHOULDN'T A DONE IT, CHILDREN! I'M TOUCHED..!

WORZEL'S DISAPPOINTMENT WAS VERY PLAIN TO SEE!

OO, AR! AH-HEM! EE GOT 'EM MIXED UP, DIDN'T EE?

NO- THEY'RE FOR YOU!

BE GRATEFUL, WORZEL GUMMIDGE - IT IS CHRISTMAS! IT'S THE THOUGHT THAT COUNTS!

TYPICALLY GUMMIDGE, THE SCARECROW HAD TO SEE WHAT ELSE WAS BEING GIVEN AWAY...

I'LL JUST EXCHANGE THESE FOR...

YOU WILL NOT! I'M SORRY WE BOTHERED TO GET SOME-THING FOR YOU!

ALL I ASK IS AN EQUAL PICK O' THE SPOILS!

SPOILS? BE THANKFUL YOU'VE GOT A WARM SCARF AND SOME ORANGES!

LEAVING THE CHILDREN, WORZEL SET OUT FOR THE VILLAGE...

CHRISTMAS IS A TIME FOR GIVIN'- AN' GETTIN' TAIN'T FITTIN' SO MUCH IS GIVIN' TO 'EM WHAT AIN'T NEEDIN'...

THE FIRST HOUSE WORZEL CAME TO WAS BRIGHTLY LIT AND FILLED WITH CHRISTMAS TRIMMINGS!

OOO! 'OW ABOUT THAT! WHO COULD BLAME A STEWPIT OLD SCARECROW IF 'E THOUGHT ALL THOSE PRESENTS WERE FOR 'IM?

LATER, THAT SAME DAY, THE GOOD PEOPLE OF SCATTERBROOK GATHERED OUTSIDE THE VILLAGE SCHOOL...

WE SHOULD CALL THE POLICE! IT'S A CRYING SHAME — STEALING ALL OUR GIFTS! FROM OUR OWN HOMES, TOO!

MRS. BLOOMSBURY-BARTON IS *HOPPING* MAD!

CAN YOU BLAME HER?

I'VE A SNEAKING SUSPICION THAT, SOMEHOW, WORZEL GUMMIDGE IS MIXED UP IN THIS!

I'VE BEEN HAVING THE SAME THOUGHT! BUT WHY WOULD HE WANT THEIR PRESENTS?

ALL THOSE IN FAVOUR, HANDS UP!

NOT FAR AWAY...

BEATS ME WHY'D A-BODY'D WANT THESE! RUBBISH, AN' FIT FOR NUTHIN' SAVE MEBBE PUTTIN' IN A DRAWER FOR NEXT YEAR!

WITH HIS CURIOSITY SATISFIED, WORZEL REWRAPPED THE GIFTS...

...AND DECIDED TO RETURN EACH TO ITS RIGHTFUL PLACE UNDER A CHRISTMAS TREE!

WORKING SILENTLY AS A SCARECROW CAN, WORZEL MADE HIS SANTA CLAUS ROUNDS...

A GOOD JOB I'VE ME THINK-HEAD ON 'COS IT'D BE AWFUL IF I GETS THE WRONG ADDRESS!

NOT EVERYONE, THOUGH, AGREED WITH WORZEL'S HIGH OPINION OF HIS MEMORY! NOR HIS PACKAGING SKILLS!

AND WHAT IDIOT EVER WRAPPED A MESS LIKE THIS?

THESE AREN'T OURS!

WITH JUST THREE MORE HOUSES TO VISIT, WORZEL WAS CAUGHT IN THE ACT OF ENTERING...

NOT THIS TIME, WORZEL!

YEOOW! OO, AR! IT'S A FAIR COP... HEY, IT'S YOU TWO!

WHAT ON EARTH ARE YOU DOING?

TAIN'T MY FAULT THAT STEWPIT... ER, AR... SOME PEOPLE DON'T HAVE ANY IDEA 'OW TO GIVE PRESENTS, IS IT? ALL I WANTED WAS A PIPE, AN' CHOCS, AN' A NICE BIG CHEESE!

HE'S AN INFERNAL MIXER BUT HE ISN'T REALLY A BAD, BAD LAD!

LET'S TRICK THE OLD BUZZARD! LET'S ... WHISSSSS-WHISSSSS-WHISSSSS!

I CAN'T 'EAR! WHY'S SHE A-WHISPERIN'?

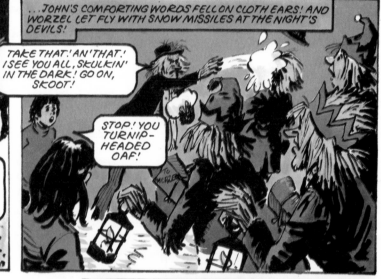

MEMORY TEST

Study closely this colourful country scene for two minutes (or a slow count to 100). Then turn to page 59 for a memory test.

FARMER FUN

THEN and NOW - on the farm

Ploughing

Potato picking

Forestry

Harvesting

Crop-spraying

Milk transportation

MISTER GUMMIDGE

THE countryside looked wonderful. Just like in a painting with many colours splashed over the hedgerows and on the bushes. Those gardens belonging to the scattered farms were a mass of gorgeous blooms. Even the people of Scatterbrook seemed in tune with the season, wearing light, colourful clothes.

For Worzel Gummidge, though, the time of year meant nothing. His clothes did not alter. He did not visit a shop or a tailor and have the latest fashions designed especially for him. What he wore was what Mr. Crowman or Farmer Braithewaite wanted him to wear and that usually meant somebody else's cast-offs.

Overhead, the rooks flew in their monotonous circles. Several lone birds made detours when they reached Worzel's scarecrow pole. One, singing lustily as it passed, was a great feathered colour flash and Worzel envied it with all his stuffed heart. In fact, he became so envious that he eased himself off the pole and stomped towards the gate leading out of Ten Acre Field. He had to get something different to wear – and he knew exactly where to find a change of clothes . . .

Mrs. Bloomsbury-Barton, at this time of year, was already making plans for the coming winter. She did not believe in waiting until the last minute. She liked to be prepared. And Gummidge was very thankful that she was such a meticulous, far-sighted person.

When he reached Mrs. Bloomsbury-Barton's residence, Worzel went straight round the back. He was careful not to be seen. What he had in mind meant bending some of the rules – people's rules. Not scarecrow rules. Of course, he was cunning enough to know that breaking people's rules – or bending them, as he liked to call his deviations – applied to scarecrows given the ability to walk and talk. So Mr. Crowman said, and Mr. Crowman ruled every scarecrow roost.

But Worzel felt that he was special. Able to take some small liberties. Like when he opened the door of Mrs. Bloomsbury-Barton's garden shed and spied her collection of clothing.

A few minutes later, Worzel peered into the shed's glass side and postured. He loved his new hat with its little green feather in the band. And that cravat in bright blue with yellow polka-dots really did something for him. He wished, though, that the tweed jacket fitted better. He would have been a sight in that walking across the fields.

Sighing, Worzel sadly left the jacket and, instead, settled for a new pair of tan slacks.

John and Sue were taking a short cut to the schoolhouse when they spotted Worzel furtively creeping from Mrs. Bloomsbury-Barton's garden.

"What's he up to?" John asked, wondering what seemed so different about the scarecrow.

Sue started, unable to believe her eyes. "He's . . . those . . . Oh, the sneaky rascal!"

"Please explain in English," John told her.

"Worzel," Sue exclaimed. "He's only been and taken some of Mrs. Bloomsbury-Barton's collection of cast-off clothes – the ones she saves for jumble sales in the winter."

"He's looking smart enough to go to the garden fete," said John. "But he doesn't even know there is one!"

The day which had started so brilliantly suddenly changed. A fast moving dark cloud swept across the land and, away in the distance, the rumble of thunder announced a summer storm. Within minutes, rain began to fall.

Worzel glared at the sky and shook his fist at the menacing clouds. His new hat already looked decrepit and those lovely tan slacks sagged in sodden dismay. As for the cravat, its yellow polka-dot spots were decidedly green now as the bright blue ran.

Not many people stayed out of doors in the storm and Worzel took the opportunity to wander down the village streets. A scarecrow had to accept all weathers – it was part and parcel of the job. As he passed shop windows displaying all kinds of summer-weight clothes, Worzel felt tempted. He searched his voluminous pockets. They were crammed with treasures saved from various escapades but the one thing he did not find was money. And he knew that those lovely clothes could not be bought without money.

Shrugging, Worzel continued along the street. His mouth watered when he came to the baker's and saw all those cream cakes and chocolate eclairs in the window. He hurried then, not daring to look into the green-grocers. He did not enjoy seeing turnips and cabbages and the like on sale. He had a vivid imagination and it did strange things to his system knowing that some people cooked turnips . . .

At the corner of the street, Worzel ducked into a doorway. He was soaked, beginning to bend with the weight of water in his insides. Five large cars slowly approached, each one filled with local big-wigs. And all of them wore their best clothes, the women especially ravishing in swirling dresses and large floral hats.

Watching the cars, Worzel wondered what they were doing out in the downpour. When they turned into the school gates, he was even more interested. He waited to see how they coped getting out in the rain but just at that very moment the dark clouds scurried away and the sun shone again.

It was unbelievable how fast people appeared. They came from shops and houses and flocked to the school. Children in their Sunday best skipped along after parents, carefully avoiding rain puddles.

Shaking himself, Worzel stepped from the doorway and joined the tail end of the crowd. Steam rose from him as the sun grew hotter and began to dry him out.

John tugged at Sue's arm and pointed. "It's Worzel – doesn't he look bedraggled?"

Sue felt sorrow for the scarecrow. How different he looked from the 'natty' gent she'd seen sneaking from Mrs. Bloomsbury-Barton's shed. "Does he know what's going on?" she asked John.

"Nothing about Worzel would surprise me," the boy replied.

Sue slipped away from the others and went straight to Gummidge. "Isn't it a lovely day?" she asked the scarecrow.

Worzel sulked. He felt uncomfortable. And more to the point, he needed to know what was going on to satisfy his curiosity.

"Luverly? What's luverly 'bout gettin' soaked?"

"You're drying fast," Sue remarked. "And where did you get those nice new clothes?" She wanted to hear his explanation.

Worzel's expression said it all. He was not telling. Instead, he asked, "Am I invited?"

"Invited?" Sue sounded puzzled. Then, she noticed Worzel's gaze and realised he meant invited to the party. "Hardly, Worzel," she said. "Scarecrows aren't usually asked to a fete."

"I am arskt everywheres," Gummidge stated firmly, daring her to refute that fact. "Fete, eh? Ar, ee knows if they're havin' cakes an' things?"

Sue did know. "Yes, but for the special guests only."

"Special? What's special 'bout 'em?" Worzel pointed at a bunch of locals standing round a fat man in tweeds.

John came up and grinned. "You're a sight, Worzel," he said. "What have you been doing? – washing in blue dye?"

Sue kicked him on the ankle but, luckily, Gummidge was not listening. He was far too interested in the fat man and the way the people paid him unstinting respect.

"No, Worzel!" John said quite firmly.

Gummidge tore his mind from the fat man and glared at John. "Eh, what?" he asked.

"I said 'No!', Worzel," the boy repeated.

"No what? I swears on a wheatsheaf you're gettin' worse'n me for double-talkin'," the scarecrow said.

"I meant you can't get your fingers into the food," John explained.

The sun had completely dried him now and Worzel felt better. So much so that without a word he ambled away from the children and joined the crowd harkening to the fat man's every word. Naturally, Worzel did not know who the man was but he soon got the impression of a stuff-shirt and big-head lapping up this uncalled for adulation.

"If Worzel speaks . . ." John whispered to Sue.

Worzel had no intention of talking. Listening, for once, was more informative. He kept hearing different people saying, 'Very nice, Mister Watson', or 'Are you in favour, Mister Watson?'. No matter what was said it was always 'Mister Watson'.

The fat man's eyes flatly surveyed Worzel Gummidge. As M.P. for Scatterbrook and district he liked to pride himself on instantly recognizing every voter. But this person . . . His face wrinkled in puzzlement. He tried to avoid certain tricky questions and get into a conversation with the stranger but by the time he had answered a farmer's complaint, Worzel had departed for more likely fields.

The scarecrow never failed to seize a chance for a free meal. The second a buxom lady opened the school doors and Worzel saw trestle-tables groaning beneath the weight of salads, cakes and biscuits he was off like a shot. But this was not his moment of glory. The same buxom lady stood guard over the door and frowned at the intruder.

"Yes?" she enquired as Worzel tried to push past. "Do you have an invitation card?"

This flummoxed the scarecrow. "I'm Mister Gummidge," he said in his poshest accent.

"And I'm the Queen of Sheba," the woman snorted in disapproval. "It doesn't matter who you say you are you can't get in without an invitation. Them's rules!"

"Does Mister Watson 'ave one?" Worzel asked, eyes bulging as he surveyed the eats.

"He does," came the short reply. And the lady blocked the entire doorway so that the scarecrow was even denied a peep of the spread.

Dismayed, downhearted and rather fed-up, Worzel Gummidge retreated. He did not accept defeat lightly, though. His devious mind had a way of turning up trumps when he had his stomach set on fillers. He searched his pockets in hope. Surely he owned something which could be traded for an invitation! All he had was an old handkerchief, an apple core, a worm which wriggled and tried to get at the apple core, bits of fancy paper, a few nuts without bolts, baling wire and an old orange skin he had been saving for Aunt Sally's next pudding making effort.

"Don't feel blue," John said, coming to join Gummidge. "We're not getting anything to eat, either."

"I'm'se good as 'em," Worzel said. He glared at the fat man who was surrounded by an even larger audience. "He talks rubbish an' not decent rubbish."

John laughed. Mr. Watson, M.P. would not like hearing Worzel's estimation of his vocalizations. "Mr. Watson is a very distinguished person in Westminster," he said.

Worzel Gummidge knew that some clocks chimed and these chimes were called *Westminster*. "Cos he lives in a clock don't make

'im dist . . . what you said.''

John did not quite connect a clock with the M.P. but decided not to press the issue. Instead, he pointed at another man who stood head-and-shoulders over the giggling ladies hanging on his every word. "That's Lord Seabottom – he's a landowner and chairman of the education authority," he informed the scarecrow.

"Eddykation?" Worzel wondered what a man like that was doing with grown-ups. He had been to the Scarecrow school but they never had nobody quite like this tall, lean man.

"Oh, he's dropped his ticket . . ." John started to move towards Lord Seabottom but found Gummidge ahead of him. He watched with a wry smile as the scarecrow bent and swiftly pocketed the landowner's invitation. He imagined all sorts of uproar when Worzel tried to gain an entrance using that particular identification. And he called Sue to see the fun.

Worzel Gummidge was not a fool. He had no intention of confronting the buxom lady again, so he hung around the school door until she was called to attend to a group of VIP's and a replacement 'guard' took over. Then . . .

The friendly, pleasant-faced woman wearing a floppy hat glanced at Worzel's invitation and not at his features. The name she read gave her quite a thrill and she curtsied, and said, "It's an honour, your lordship . . ."

Her pride was short-lived. Gummidge zoomed past and made straight for the trestle-table containing the favourite scarecrow treat – chocolate cake oozing with cream.

"Well, I never!" Sue gasped. "He's got the cheek of the devil."

"He's got nerve and a brass neck," John said.

Worzel had cake which pleased him more than cheek or nerve. He totally ignored the furtive glances of others in the room and made a pig of himself going from table to table. Only when he felt too full to run did he stop eating. And then he just had to sample the fizzy drinks . . .

"I say, old chap," a voice said from Worzel's rear. "Don't they feed you at the jolly old homestead?"

Worzel did not like the newcomer's accent or the way those pale, watery eyes stared at him. Quite deliberately he upturned his glass and a cascade of fizzy drink went all over the other. Hiding a grin, Worzel ambled to the door and made a splendid exit.

John held his sides and chortled, "Oh, Worzel – you were magnificent!"

"Call me Mister Gummidge, please" the scarecrow replied.

Sue rolled her eyes heavenwards. "He's been entertained and overfed and now he wants to be treated like visiting royalty," she said with a tone of some admiration.

"Why *Mister* Gummidge?" John asked.

Worzel drew his jacket tighter around his body. "Only the best gets to eat an' I had choklit cake. That makes ee lesser'n me an' gets me a Mister 'fore Gummidge."

"He has a point, John," Sue said.

"On his head," John snorted.

Worzel ignored the children. Walking erect, he went across the school grounds, passing knots of people as if he was the most important person who had ever been invited to a fete's private 'tent'. And as he nodded regally to each group he muttered, "*Mister* Gummidge, please."

He felt so good! So very good! Almost as good as a lord! He'd put Mrs. Bloomsbury-Barton's old clothes back – he felt important enough to only wear *UNIFORMS* from now on.

Memory picture questions...

1. ONE HORSE WAS WHITE, THE OTHER WAS . . . . ?
2. HOW MANY TRACTORS WERE IN THE PICTURE . . . . ?
3. WHAT COLOUR WAS THE FARM LORRY . . . . ?
4. HOW MANY COWS WERE IN THE FIELD . . . . ?
5. WHAT LIVESTOCK WAS IN THE FRONT GARDEN OF THE FARM . . . . ?
6. HOW MANY GATES WERE SHOWN IN THE PICTURE . . . . ?
7. WHAT WAS HANGING OVER THE FRONT DOOR OF THE FARMHOUSE . . . . ?
8. WAS THERE A SCARECROW IN THE PICTURE . . . . ?
9. HOW MANY MILK CHURNS WERE IN VIEW . . . . ?
10. WHICH OF THESE ANIMALS WAS **NOT** IN THE PICTURE – A FOX OR A RABBIT . . . . ?

YOUR ANSWERS: 1. _____   2. _____
3. _____   4. _____   5. _____
6. _____   7. _____   8. _____
9. _____   10. _____

ALL THE ANSWERS

IDENTITY PARADE: 1, WEASEL. 2, HARVEST MOUSE. 3, COMMON LIZARD.
4, ADDER.   5, COMMON FROG.   6, PINE MARTEN.   7, SHORT-TAILED VOLE.
8, RABBIT.   9. FALLOW DEER.   10, PHEASANT.

SPOT THE DIFFERENCE :
1. BUSH BY POND. 2. FURROW ON FIELD. 3. LEAF FROM LOG.
4. SMALL LOG. 5, FLOWER IN FOREGROUND. 6, STONE.
7, BRICKS IN FARMHOUSE WALL. 8, CHURCH CLOCK.
9, CHIMNEY STACK. 10, BIRD.

TREES: 1, SPRUCE. 2, COMMON OAK.
3, SILVER BIRCH. 4, HORNBEAM.
5, SCOTS PINE. 6, MOUNTAIN ASH.
7, LOMBARDY POPLAR. 8, SWEET CHESTNUT. 9, FIELD ELM. 10, HOLLY.
11, CEDAR. 12, LARCH.

OUT OF ORDER:
B–D–A–C

AUNT SALLY DOUBLES:
2 – 4

X- WORD.
ACROSS: 2, COWSHED 4, SHEEP 7, DRESS
9, LADDER 10, MILK CHURN 12,
KITTEN 13, OWL 14, DOG 16, GNAT
18, MOLE 19, RAM 20, SHEEPSHEARER
21, HEN 23, TRACTOR 24, BARN
26, FARMHOUSE 28, WATER TROUGH
29, SUN
DOWN: 1, SPUR 2, COMBINE HARVESTER
3, EWE 5, HEDGETRIMMER
6, FLASK 7, DUCKPOND 8, STRAW
11, KEG 15, PIGSTY 16, GEESE
17, FARMER 21, HORSES 22, DRAKE
25, COW 27, HOG.

MEMORY:
1. BROWN
2. TWO
3. BLUE
4. FOUR
5. A DUCK
6. FIVE
7. HORSESHOE
8. YES
9. THREE
10. RABBIT

59

THE STAR TURN

ONE MORNING IN TEN ACRE FIELD...

I WISH EVERY DAY WAS A HOLIDAY FOR 'IM WHAT OWNS THE FARM! NO PRETENDIN' TO SCARE THOSE FEATHERED ROOK FOOLS AN' NOBODY CHASIN' AFTER THE SILLY MOOS!

SUDDENLY THE PEACE WAS SHATTERED...

...AND AS THE HELICOPTER SWEPT PAST, WORZEL FELT HE WAS BEING BLOWN APART!

AFTER A MAGNIFICENT DISPLAY THE HELICOPTER LANDED JUST OUTSIDE THE VILLAGE...

HURRY... LET'S GET DOWN THERE!

HI, KIDS — THIS HERE IS MISTER McGUIRE... THE MISTER McGUIRE, MOVIE-MAKER!